The _____ to:

_____

D0337109

WITHDRAWN
FROM STOCK

Note to parents and carers

Many children are now taught to read using the phonic approach. This means they are taught to look at the letters, say the sounds, and then blend them to make a word. So, for example, children blend **c/a/t** to make the word **cat**, and **sh/o/p** to make **shop**.

When children have completed their initial phonics learning, they are ready to apply it to reading real books. Ladybird's **Superhero Phonic Readers** are planned for this exciting stage.

Some words are hard to read using beginner phonics. These words are often known as 'tricky words'. Some of these occur frequently in the English language so it is useful for children to memorize them.

Have fun doing our Tricky Words Memory Quiz on page 30. This features the most useful tricky words from the story.

How to use Superhero Phonic Readers:

- Start at level one and gradually progress through the series. Each story is a little bit longer than the last and uses more grown-up vocabulary.
- Children will be able to read **Superhero Phonic Readers** for themselves. Let your child read to you, and share the excitement!
- If your child finds any words difficult, help him or her to work out the sounds in the word.
- Early readers can be concentrating so hard on the words that they sometimes don't fully grasp the overall meaning of what they read. The puzzle questions on pages 28 and 29 will help with this. Have fun talking about them together.
- There is a reward chart at the back of the book – young readers can fill this in and add stickers to it.
- The Ladybird website **www.ladybird.com** features a wealth of information about phonics and reading.
- Enjoy reading together!

Geraldine Taylor
Ladybird Educational Consultant

Laois County Library
Leabharlann Chontae Laoise

Acc. No. .... D⌒ ....

Class No. .... JPB ....

Inv. No. ....

LEABHARLANN CHONTAE LAOISE

Acc. No. ...... OON .... Class No. ...... JPB

DATE OF RETURN	DATE OF RETURN	DATE OF RETURN

1 ___ 2022

Educat

Pho

Superhero
Phonic Readers

Cow Boy

written by Dick Crossley

illustrated by Mark Ruffle

Billy was mad about cowboys.

He liked cowboy stuff best.

He had a cool cowboy hat,

cool cowboy boots,

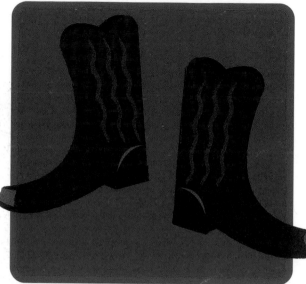

a cool sheriff's star,

and cool cowboy water pistols.

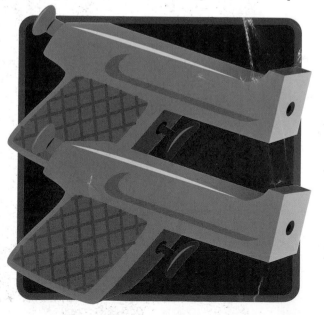

"When I grow up," said Billy to his mum,
"I will be the best cowboy ever!"

He told his dad, too.

Dad smiled at Billy. He gave Billy a bottle of milk.
It had a magic pink glow.
"Drink this," said Dad, with a wink.

Billy was puzzled. But that night, he drank a glass of the magic pink milk with his supper.

When he woke up the next morning, his dream had come true! He was a cool cowboy.

Well, sort of.

Billy had turned into a superhero on hooves – Cow Boy!

As Cow Boy, Billy could do fantastic things.
He spent the morning trying out his new moves –
with his new hooves!

15

In the afternoon, he trotted into town to stop crime.

His pistols did not shoot water, they shot milkshake.

But it was not just normal milkshake.
Banana milkshake did this…

Strawberry milkshake did this...

19

And chocolate milkshake…

…well, it was just chocolate milkshake.

Billy's tail was cool, too.

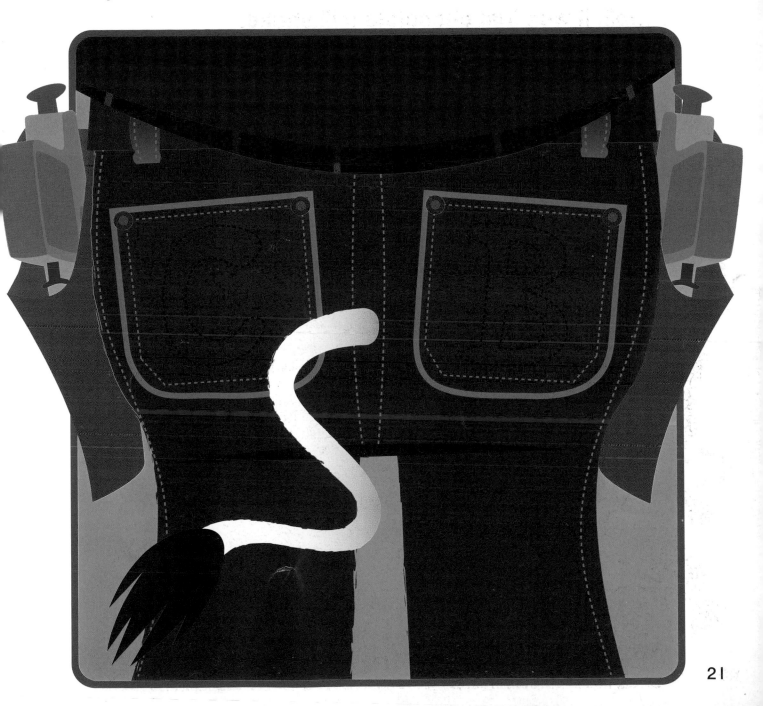

He could make it as long as he needed it to be,

to help people,

to tie up crooks,

or to swing from.

Being a superhero was fun. But it was hard work, too. Billy was not too sad when the magic wore off.

He went home for a rest – and to play at being a normal cowboy sheriff.

"A drop more?" asked Dad, the next morning.
Billy smiled at him, but shook his head.

"Maybe another day," he said...

Superhero Secret Puzzles

★ What cowboy stuff did Billy have?

★ What did Dad give Billy?

★ What happened when Billy drank the magic milk?

★ What flavours of milkshake can Cow Boy's pistols shoot?

★ What can Cow Boy use his tail for?

★ If you could be part-animal for a day, what would you be?

Look at these pictures from the story and say the order they should go in.

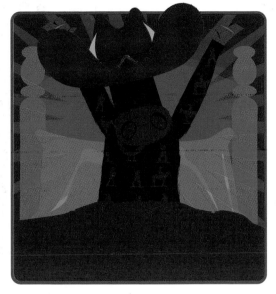

A

B

C

D

Answer on page 30.

Tricky Words Memory Quiz

Can you remember these words from the story?

See if you can read them super-fast.

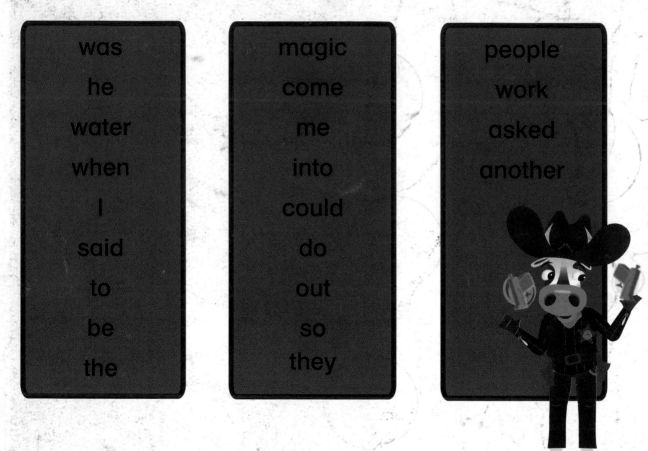

was	magic	people
he	come	work
water	me	asked
when	into	another
I	could	
said	do	
to	out	
be	so	
the	they	

What else can you remember?

Can you put the book down and say what happens in the story?

I'm a phonic Superhero

I can read all of **Cow Boy**.

I can read all the tricky words.

By _____

Date _____

level 4

Ask an adult to cut this page out for you. You can stick it on your wall.